Ulf Löfgren

and the magic wand

Macdonald

One day, when Albin was out for a walk, he saw
a balloon floating by. In the basket underneath,
there was a little old man. As he waved to Albin,
something dropped from his hand.

Albin was about to pick it up,
when the little old man shouted:
'Stop! Don't touch it! It's a magic wand
but it's broken, so all its magic goes wrong . . .
especially if you talk in rhymes!'

3

When the old man had gone, Albin looked down
at the magic wand. It certainly was broken,
and someone had tied it together with string.

Albin waved it about.
It shook and rattled.
'What harm can
this old thing do?'
said Albin. 'If I say . . .
rabbit with a habit,
I'm sure nothing will happen.'

5

'And just what do *you* want?'
said the huge rabbit
who stood at Albin's side.
'Oh . . . er . . . I was just
trying out this magic wand,'
said Albin, 'but I think
there's something wrong
with it.'

6

'Well, of course, there is,'
said the rabbit crossly,
'or it wouldn't make
a giant rabbit like me!'
And he stomped off in a huff.
'I'll try again,' said Albin.
'Giraffe in a scarf!'

At once, three tiny giraffes appeared.
'You've got it wrong again!' they shouted.
'We are far too small.'

The three giraffes galloped away.
'Perhaps I can get it right this time,' said Albin.
'What if I say . . . *fish on a dish?*'

A very strange fish appeared.
'Your wand can't make up
its mind,' it said.
'What am I supposed to be,
a fish or a bird?'

The fish-bird
stalked off angrily.
Oh, dear, nothing
was going right!
'Perhaps I'll have
better luck if I say . . .
cat in a hat!' said Albin.

11

Well, Albin did get a cat in a hat . . .
but it was the strangest cat he had ever seen!
'What have you done to me?' the cat said.
'I look ridiculous! Even my mother wouldn't recognize me!'
'I'm so sorry,' said Albin. 'It's this broken wand . . .'

'What broken wand? And where did you get
that funny-looking cat?' said a voice.
It was Albin's friend, Ferdinand.

'Well,' Albin explained,
'I found this magic wand,
you see . . . but it's broken
so all its spells go wrong,
especially rhyming ones!'

'Hmm, it's broken alright . . .
let me try,' said Ferdinand.
'I think I'll just magic up
some money.
*Big, brave and bold,
a sack full of gold!*'

'What's this?' cried Ferdinand. 'All I've got
is a sack of potatoes!'

'What I would really like now is some ice cream,'
said Albin. '*I dream of ice cream!*'

'Ugh!' said Albin. 'It's hot ice cream!
I don't want any of that!'

'Perhaps the wand would make me a horse to ride on,'
said Ferdinand. '*A real horse, of course!*'

19

'Oh, no, I don't fancy riding on a hippo,'
said Ferdinand.

'Well, I didn't get my ice cream, and I'm still hungry,' said Albin. '*Magic wand please make a juicy hot pancake.*'

'I said a hot pancake, not hot soup!
I hate fish soup!' wailed Albin.
'You know, Ferdinand, this wand is no good.
I think we should find that little old man
and give the wand back.'